D0240626

This Princess Annual belongs to Princess ~~Zara~~

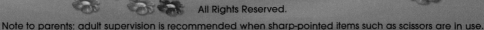

EGMONT

We bring stories to life

First published in Great Britain in 2008 by Egmont UK Limited,
239 Kensington High Street, London W8 6SA.

© Disney Enterprises, Inc.

Editor: Sally Gilbert
Art Editor: Alexandra Chamadia
Designer: Jaymala Raval
Photography: Laura Ashman

ISBN 978 1 4052 3905 9
1 3 5 7 9 10 8 6 4 2
Printed in Italy.

All Rights Reserved.

Note to parents: adult supervision is recommended when sharp-pointed items such as scissors are in use.

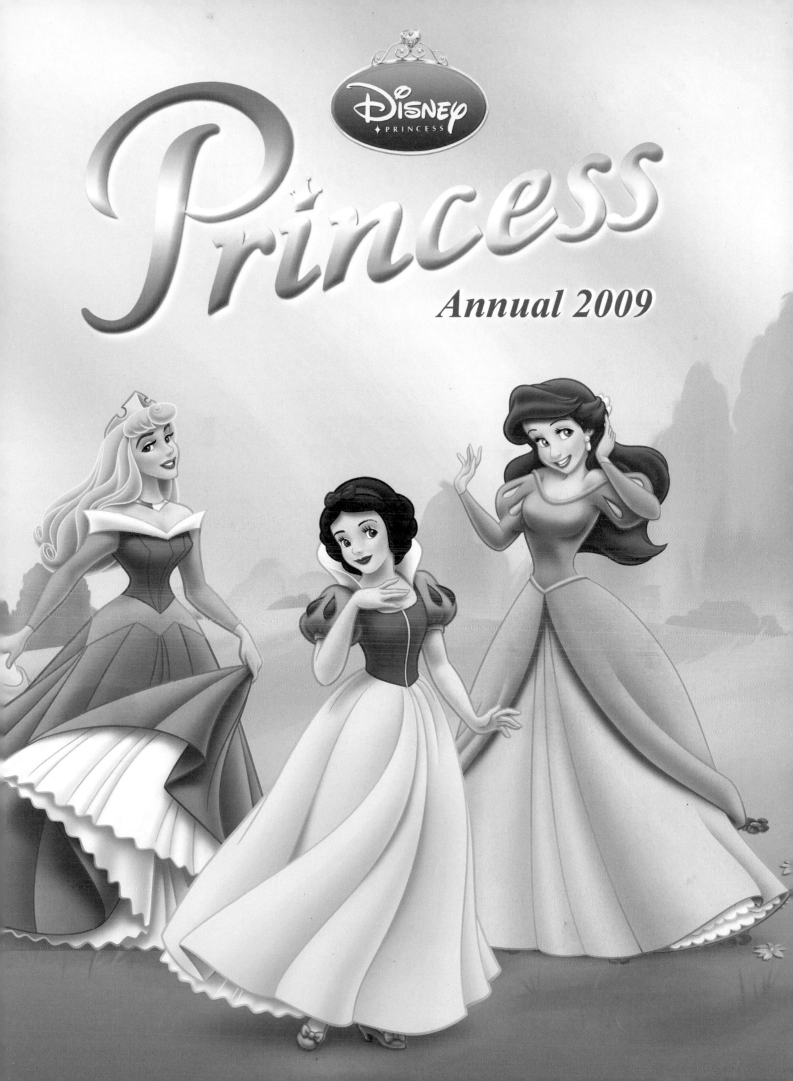

Once upon a time, in fairy-tale kingdoms far away, there lived six beautiful princesses.

Turn the page to begin the fairy tale ...

Aurora Factfile

Read some royal facts about Princess Aurora.

Personality: Aurora is a beautiful girl with a lovely voice and natural grace.

Friends: Aurora has three Fairy Godmothers, Merryweather, Flora and Fauna, who love Aurora like a daughter.

Family: Aurora is the daughter of King Stefan and his queen.

Romance: Prince Phillip is Aurora's true love.

Princess
Aurora

Magical Mischief

1 One evening, Aurora and Prince Phillip hosted a ball. One of their guests was keeping everyone entertained. "That elf's a bit cheeky," laughed the Prince, as everyone watched him chase Merryweather.

2 When the elf grew tired of teasing Merryweather, he cast a spell on Aurora and Prince Phillip while they were dancing.

3 The spell caused Aurora's ballgown to magically turn into a suit of armour! "Oh, dear!" laughed the fairies.

4 When the spell wore off, the elf cast a love spell on the royal couple instead. "I feel all funny," said the Prince.

5 The love spell made Prince Phillip give Aurora lots of presents. First, he gave her a beautiful necklace.

6 Then he gave her a lovely gold teapot. "It's beautiful!" cried Aurora.

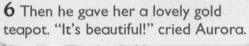

7 Meanwhile, the fairies were getting annoyed with the elf. "I'm not being naughty!" laughed the elf. "Aurora is getting really nice presents!"

8 The fairies sternly told the elf never to mess with true love, so he removed the spell. "Spoil sports!" he fumed.

9 But with the spell broken, Aurora and Prince Phillip looked more in love than ever.

10 "Love has its own magic!" said Merryweather in delight. Even the elf agreed that Aurora and the Prince's love could overcome any magic spell.

The End

© 2008 Disney

Add a design to Aurora's gown and then finish
colouring in this picture.

13

Heart Headdress

Make and wear Aurora's headdress - it will be dear to your princess heart.

You will need:

scissors

glue

headband

ribbon

felt hearts

jewels

14

1 Wrap a length of ribbon around an old headband and glue it in place.

2 Decorate the headband by sticking on felt hearts and jewels. Leave to dry, before wearing your headdress like a true princess.

Woodland Wonders

Aurora is counting woodland creatures in the forest.

Write how many of each creature there are in the hearts at the bottom of the page.

Answers:
Rabbits - 2, squirrels - 3, deer - 1, birds - 4.

Aurora's Muddle

Oh dear, the fairies have magically mixed up the order of the story.

Write the correct order in the hearts at the bottom of the page.

1

2

3

4

Snow White Factfile

Learn all about lovely and sweet Snow White.

Personality: Gentle and loveable nature.

Friends: The Seven Dwarfs: Happy, Doc, Grumpy, Bashful, Sneezy, Sleepy and Dopey.

Family: Snow White is the stepdaughter of the wicked queen.

Romance: The handsome Prince sweeps Snow White off her feet.

Princess
Snow White

Forest Celebration

1 When Snow White's village was 500 years old, the Mayor wanted to celebrate. "We'll have a fireworks display at the palace and invite everyone," he told Snow White and the Prince.

2 As work for the fireworks display began, Snow White told the Prince, "I'm worried that these noisy fireworks will frighten the animals and they won't want to come."

3 Later, Snow White asked the forest animals about the fireworks. "Oh, you poor things, you are scared," said Snow White.

4 Concerned, Snow White and the Prince leapt on to their horse and rode to the Dwarfs' cottage.

5 The Dwarfs were pleased to see the royal couple. Snow White told them all about the firework display and the animals. "What can we do?" she asked.

6 "Maybe we should hold our own celebration here in the forest," suggested Doc. "It can be animal-friendly." "What a good idea!" cried Snow White.

7 So they all set about planning their forest celebration. "There can be music and dancing," said Sneezy. "And gooseberry pie," added Grumpy.

8 On the day of the village fireworks, Snow White had prepared food and hung decorations around the Dwarfs' garden. "It's time for our village celebration!" she called.

9 At once, the Dwarfs started playing their musical instruments and everyone danced and sang. News of the festival soon spread to all of the forest animals.

10 What a great time they all had! When the Seven Dwarfs sat down to dinner that evening, they didn't mind that they had missed the village fireworks. "Nature is far more colourful," they all agreed.

The End

22

© 2008 Disney

Finish colouring in this picture of Snow White.

Treasure Box

Make this box to store all your princess secrets.

You will need:

glue

scissors

matchbox

wrapping paper

sequins   jewels

1 Neatly cover a matchbox with pretty wrapping paper.

2 Decorate the box by sticking on sequins and jewels. Store all your tiny princess treasures and secrets inside.

Snow White says:
Line the inside of the box with fabric for the final princess touch.

25

Forest Fun

These pictures look the same but there are six changes in the lower one. Can you spot them all?

Colour in a heart at the bottom of the page as you find each one.

Answers: The yellow butterfly has disappeared, the red butterfly has changed colour, Snow White's headband is missing, the tree on the right is missing, the purple flower is now pink and a pink bird has appeared.

Makeover Game

Snow White is getting ready to meet the Prince. Play this game with a friend to help finish her outfit.

Player 1

1
2
3
4
5
6

Player 2

1
2
3
4
5
6

How to play

You will need: coloured pens or pencils and paper. First decide who will be player 1 and who will be player 2. Cut a sheet of paper into six pieces. Write a number on each piece, from one to six. Fold the pieces of paper and put them into an empty bag. Then take it in turns to pull a piece of paper from the bag. Read the number on the piece of paper and then return it to the bag. The number shows you which section to colour in on your picture. If you choose a number you have had before, miss a turn. The player to complete her picture first is the winner!

Cinderella Factfile

Read all about gentle and kind Cinderella.

Personality: Intelligent and hardworking.

Friends: Gus and Jaq, Cinderella's mice friends, care very much about Cinderella.

Family: Cinderella is the stepdaughter of Lady Tremaine and she has two stepsisters, Drizella and Anastasia.

Romance: Prince Charming is Cinderella's dream prince.

Princess
Cinderella

The Lost Sparkle

1 One day, Cinderella found a sad-looking pixie in the palace garden. "Please help me!" the pixie cried.

2 "My magical sparkle is disappearing," the pixie said, "and I'm losing my powers." Cinderella promised to help the pixie find her sparkle again.

3 Cinderella decided to look for sparkling things to help the pixie. Gus found some shiny material but that didn't seem sparkly enough.

4 Even Cinderella's brightest ballgown wasn't sparkly enough for a pixie.

5 What about your sparkling earrings, Cinderella?" asked Jaq. Cinderella suddenly had an idea. "What if the Fairy Godmother mixed all the shiny things together?" she said.

6 So Cinderella went to ask the Prince if he had anything to add. "These stars on my map twinkle," he said.

31

7 Later, the Fairy Godmother asked Cinderella to list all the shiny things. "There were the beautiful gowns, sparkling material, twinkling stars and shining earrings," Cinderella told her.

8 "Bibbidi-bobbidi-boo," the Fairy Godmother sang, as she cast her spell, using Cinderella's prettiest jewellery box to hold the sparkling magic.

9 "This magic will help the pixie," the Fairy Godmother explained. "Thank you," Cinderella replied, before returning to the pixie in the palace garden.

10 Cinderella sprinkled the magical sparkle over the pixie. "I feel wonderful," the pixie cried, as her glow returned. "Thank you, Cinderella, you're a very special friend."

The End

Colour in this magical scene of Cinderella and her prince.

© 2008 Disney

33

Jewel Ring

Create and wear Cinderella's sparkling jewel ring.

You will need:

glue

scissors

tinsel-wire

button with loop   jewels

1 Find a button with a loop and thread a length of pretty tinsel-wire through the middle.

2 Secure the tinsel-wire into a shape that will fit around your finger. Decorate the top of the button by sticking on jewels.

Cinderella says:
Make a sparkling new ring for your princess friend, too.

35

Ballgown Maze

Cinderella and her stepsisters are going to a ball.
Follow the lines to see which gown they will each be wearing.

a

b

c

Cinderella

Anastastia

Drizella

36

Answers:
Cinderella - c, Anastasia - b, Drizella - a.

Jewellery Quiz

Tick your five favourite pictures to find out the perfect piece of Cinderella's jewellery for you.

Mostly blue
You're thoughtful with a sparkling personality. So a sapphire ring is ideal for you.

Mostly green
A glowing emerald is the best item of jewellery for a kind and creative person like you.

Mostly red
You're brave and caring and deserve a noble piece of jewellery like this ruby tiara.

Jasmine Factfile

Read all about exotic and elegant Jasmine.

Personality: Fiery, courageous and intelligent.

Friends: Abu, a friendly monkey and a loyal tiger called Rajah.

Family: The Sultan of Agrabah is Jasmine's father.

Romance: Aladdin wins Jasmine's heart.

Princess
Jasmine

Dancing Princess

1 One evening, Jasmine felt bored as she watched the dancing girls at the palace. "They always dance the same steps," she thought. "If only princesses were allowed to perform – I'd spice things up!"

2 Later, Jasmine danced to music in her bedroom. "Surely no-one would recognise me if I danced at 'Dance City' in the desert," she thought.

3 So she put on a new outfit and a cloak as a disguise. Then, she slipped away from the palace to go and find Aladdin.

4 "Let's go!" Aladdin agreed when Jasmine told him her plan. And they raced across the desert to 'Dance City' in the distance.

5 "It's so much fun here," Jasmine told Aladdin, at the city. "I can dance all I like – and no-one knows I am a princess!"

6 Jasmine even got to perform on stage with the dancing girls.

7 "You are a wonderful dancer," one of the girls told Jasmine. "Please can you teach us some new steps and dance with us at the Sultan's palace later."

8 That evening, Jasmine and the dancing girls performed for the Sultan. "Who is that beautiful dancer?" the Sultan asked, pointing at Jasmine.

9 "It is me!" Jasmine told her father, removing her veil.

10 The Sultan clapped his hands in delight. "You shall perform for me all the time," he announced, giving Jasmine a golden necklace. "Princess or not!"

11 The Sultan had a great time and danced with each of the dancing girls in turn. "You're definitely my favourite dancing girl," Aladdin said to Jasmine, as he spun her around.

The End

Finish colouring in this picture of Jasmine and Rajah.

© 2008 Disney

43

Jewel Hairclip

Make and wear this butterfly and jewel hairclip.

You will need:

glue

scissors

pipe cleaner

sequins

jewels

Jasmine says:
You can make smaller butterfly hairclips, too.

1 Decorate a plain hairclip by gluing on sequins. Leave these to dry.

2 Bend a pipe cleaner into a butterfly shape and stick jewels to the centre. Finally, glue the butterfly on top of the hairclip.

Palace Pairs

Help Jasmine sort the six objects into pairs.

Which is the odd one out?

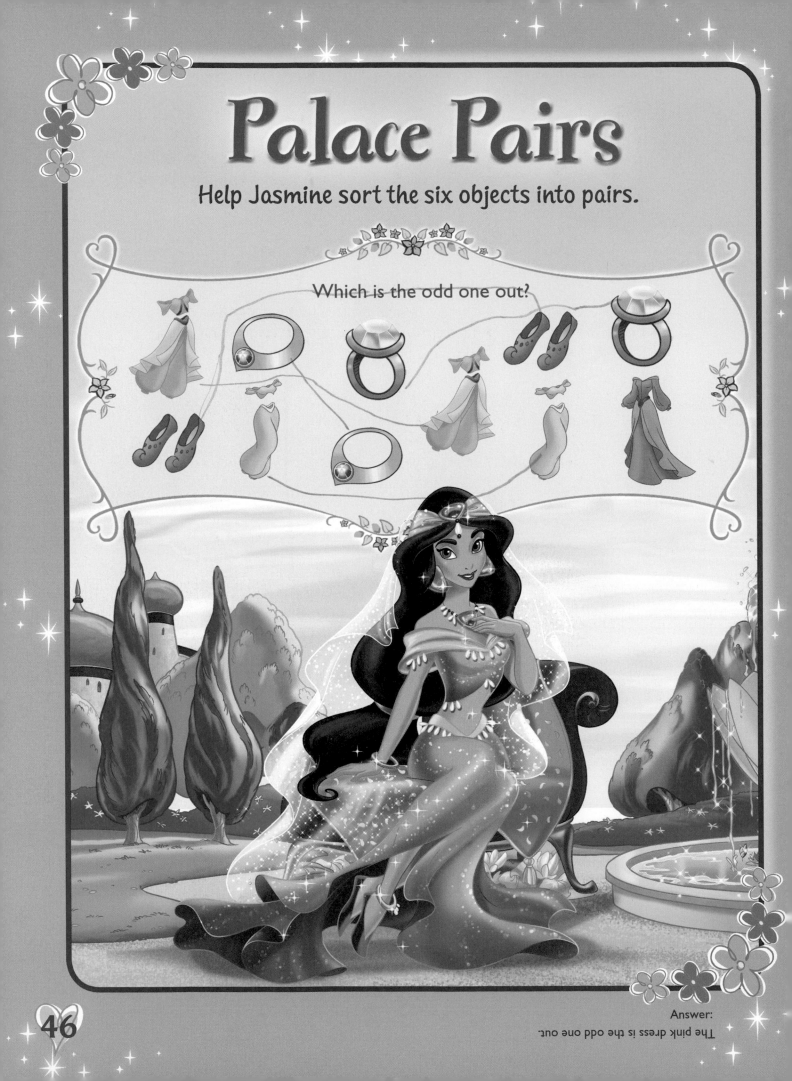

Answer:
The pink dress is the odd one out.

Perfect Outfit

Roll a dice to find the perfect
Jasmine outfit for you.

How to play

Roll a dice for each panel. Look for the item that has your number next to it and tick it off. The three items together make your perfect Jasmine outfit.

2 or 4

3 or 5

6 or 1

2 or 4

3 or 5

6 or 1

2 or 4

3 or 5

6 or 1

Ariel Factfile

Read all about your favourite mermaid - Ariel!

Personality: Fun, independent and impulsive.

Friends: Flounder is Ariel's very best friend - they have lots of fun together.

Family: King Triton is Ariel's father and Ariel has six sisters, too.

Romance: Prince Eric is Ariel's soul mate.

Princess
Ariel

Party Style

1 One day, Ariel was secretly watching the world of humans, when she saw a beautiful princess with amazing style. "I want to create a look just like hers," Ariel thought.

2 Later, Ariel tried to dress up like the princess she had seen, but when her sisters saw her they just giggled. "You look ridiculous!" they laughed.

3 Later that day, King Triton appeared. "I'm in such a good mood!" he said. "Let's have a party tonight!"

4 Ariel and Flounder swam to Ariel's bedroom to get ready for the party. "I want a stylish new look," said Ariel, "but I am all out of ideas."

5 So Ariel and Flounder swam up to the surface of the sea to watch the stylish princess again. "Maybe she can give me some fashion tips," said Ariel.

6 But before Ariel could ask the princess, a little dog appeared and chased Ariel away.

7 Suddenly, a wonderful heart-shaped locket fell into the water. "It's a gift from the princess!" said Ariel. "She wants to help me create a stylish new look for the party."

8 That evening, the guests for the party began to arrive. Word had spread that Ariel had a new look for the party and everyone was excited to see what she was going to wear.

Party at the Palace

9 Inspired by the princess's locket, Ariel was full of party outfit ideas. "That's starting to look great, Ariel," said Arista.

10 When Ariel arrived at the party, everyone was amazed by her new look. "Let's just say it's all about accessorising," Ariel smiled, as she showed off her new locket!

The End

© 2008 Disney

Colour in this magical scene of Ariel and her fishy friends. 53

Mermaid Hairstyle

Follow these steps for the perfect mermaid hairstyle!

1 Wash your hair and leave it to dry. Next, tie your hair into a high ponytail leaving some side sections hanging down.

2 Twist the ponytail into a bun and secure on the top of your head with hairpins.

3 Ask an adult to curl the side sections of your hair with curling tongs.

4 As a finishing princess touch, decorate your hairstyle with sea-flower hairbands and clips.

Underwater Shadows

Ariel is swimming through the ocean.

Can you decide which is Ariel's true shadow?

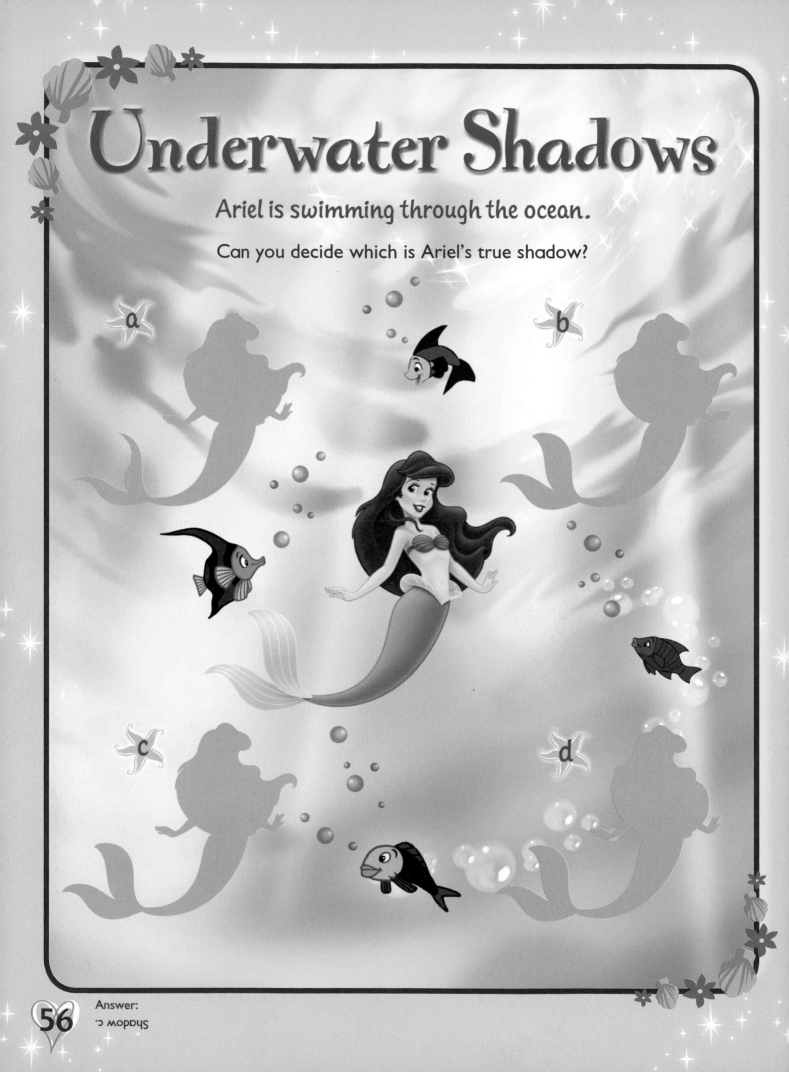

a

b

c

d

Answer:
Shadow c.

Ariel Fun

Have some underwater fun with Ariel's true or false quiz.

1 There are three fish below.

True 🤍 False 🤍

2 This is Ariel's brother, Prince Triton.

True 🤍 False 🤍

3 There is a pearl inside the oyster shell.

True 🤍 False 🤍

Answers:
1 = False, there are two. 2 = False, it is Ariel's sister, Alana. 3 = True.

Belle Factfile

Learn all about loyal and determined Belle.

Personality: Sweet, kind and patient.

Friends: The Enchanted Objects are Belle's friends. They are: Lumiere, Cogsworth, Mrs Potts, Feather Duster, Chip and Mrs Wardrobe.

Family: Her Father, Maurice, who lives in the nearby village.

Romance: Belle enjoys a romance with the Beast.

Princess
Belle

Flying High

1 One beautiful summer's day, Belle sat in the garden watching the butterflies fluttering through the air. "I'd love to fly," Belle thought to herself.

2 As Belle walked back to the castle, an old lady appeared. "May I give you some magic dust, my dear?" she asked. "It will fulfil any dream you have."

3 Later, Belle told the Beast about the lady. "I wonder if this magic dust could help me fly?" she asked him. He threw the dust over Belle and beautiful wings started to appear.

4 The wings fixed themselves to Belle and she floated up into the air. "Flying is wonderful!" she laughed.

5 "That was great fun," Belle smiled later, as she read in the library. "But to ride a flying unicorn would be truly magical."

6 So Belle blew some magic dust over her book...

7 ...and suddenly the unicorn from the book became real. It lifted both Belle and the Beast up into the air!

8 "Oh, Beast!" laughed Belle, as they soared across the sky. "Isn't flying the best thing in the world?"

9 Later that evening, Belle sat outside with the Beast. "Look at that shooting star!" she smiled. "I'd love to fly through the night sky like that."

10 "You could use the last of the magic dust," the Beast said to Belle. "Or you could see if we can find some magic of our own here in the castle!"

11 Belle followed the Beast into the castle, where he mysteriously drew back a curtain to reveal a beautiful glittering shooting-star cloak.

12 "I don't need any more magic dust to fly," Belle smiled, as she put on the shooting-star cloak. "My heart is truly flying now, I am dancing with you!"

The End

Finish colouring in this romantic picture of Belle and the Beast. 63

© 2008 Disney

Flower Bracelet

Make and wear this bracelet - it's fit for a rose princess.

You will need:

glue

scissors

fabric flower

thick ribbon

1 Cut a length of thick ribbon to go around your wrist.

2 Glue the ends together to make a band. Stick a fabric rose to the band. Place your rose band over your wrist for a pretty bracelet.

Belle says:

You can wear a matching fabric rose in your hair, too.

65

Pretty Patterns

Belle loves solving pretty princess puzzles.

Which object is missing from each sequence pattern below? Draw it in the box provided.

Answers:
1 = yellow gown, 2 = Enchanted Rose, 3 = Mrs Potts, 4 = tiara.

Belle's Tea-Time

You will need a counter each and a dice to play this tea-time treat with a friend.

Place your counters on the Start and take it in turns to throw a dice and move towards the Finish. The first player to Belle, wins!

Start

1

2

3

4

6

5

7

8

9

10

11

12

13

Finish

Princess Trivia

Now that you have read your Annual, can you match each princess to one of the following clues?

Ariel

Aurora

1 I have a pet tiger called Rajah.

2 I am friends with three Fairy Godmothers.

3 I wore glass slippers to the Ball.

4 I live in the Underwater Kingdom.

5 I have seven little friends.

6 I wear a yellow dress.

Belle

Cinderella

Jasmine

Snow White

Answers:
1 = Jasmine, 2 = Aurora, 3 = Cinderella, 4 = Ariel, 5 = Snow White, 6 = Belle.

ADVERTISEMENT

Have you seen Disney's Princess magazine?

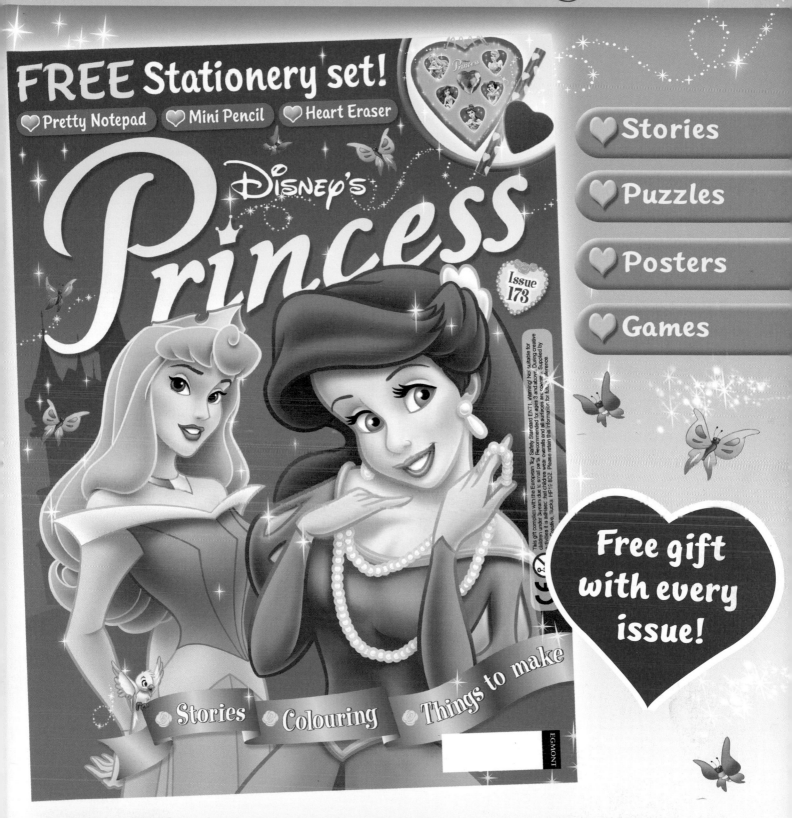

© 2008 Disney